**Edition Schott**

T0088787

## Carl Philipp Emanuel Bach
### 1714 – 1788

# Hamburger Sonate

für Flöte und Basso continuo
for Flute and Basso continuo
Cembalo (Pianoforte), Violoncello (Viola da Gamba) ad lib.

G-Dur / G major / Sol majeur

Herausgegeben von / Edited by
Kurt Walther

**FTR 1**
ISMN 979-0-001-09319-4

www.schott-music.com

Mainz · London · Berlin · Madrid · New York · Paris · Prague · Tokyo · Toronto

# Hamburger Sonate

## G-Dur / Sol majeur / G major

Herausgegeben von
Kurt Walther

(A. Wotquenne Thematisches Verzeichnis Nr. 133)

Carl Philipp Emanuel Bach
Hamburg 1786

*Das Rondo fällt ein*

Rondo
*Presto*

Das Rondo fällt ein

# Rondo

*Presto*

## Flauto

# Hamburger Sonate

G-Dur / Sol majeur / G major

(A. Wotquenne, Thematisches Verzeichnis Nr. 133)

Herausgegeben von
Kurt Walther

Carl Philipp Emanuel Bach
Hamburg 1786

*Allegretto*

# Hamburger Sonate
## G-Dur / Sol majeur / G major
(A Wotquenne, Thematisches Verzeichnis Nr. 133)

Carl Philipp Emanuel Bach
Hamburg 1786

*Das Rondo fällt ein*

## Rondo

# Flötenmusik der Mannheimer Schule · Flute Music of the Mannheim School

*Mannheimer Schule* ist seit Hugo Riemann ein Sammelbegriff für das Musikwesen der Kurpfalz unter dem von 1743–78 in Mannheim residierenden Kurfürsten Karl Theodor und für die Musiker, die in dieser Zeit in Mannheim wirkten. Hochrangige Virtuosen waren Mitglieder des Mannheimer Orchesters, von dem Charles Burney 1772 schrieb: „Es sind wirklich mehr Solospieler und Komponisten in diesem, als vielleicht in irgend einem Orchester in Europa …". „Kein Orchester der Welt hat es je dem Mannheimer zuvorgetan", so Christian Friedrich Daniel Schubart 1784. Streichinstrumente und Blasinstrumente waren im Mannheimer Orchester hervorragend besetzt.

Mit unserer Reihe *Flötenmusik der Mannheimer Schule* sollen Mannheimer Flötisten (u. a. J. Wendling und J. G. Mezger) und Komponisten, die für Flöte geschrieben haben, mit heute noch editionswürdigen Werken vorgestellt werden.

Since Hugo Riemann, the *Mannheim School* has been a term used to refer to the whole musical culture of the Palatine states under the Elector Karl Theodor, who lived in Mannheim from 1743–78, and the musicians who lived and worked in Mannheim at that time.

There were great virtuosos among the members of the Mannheim orchestra, of which Charles Burney wrote in 1772: 'Truly, there are more soloists and composers in this than perhaps in any other orchestra in Europe...'. 'No orchestra in the world has ever bettered the achievements of the Mannheim orchestra', wrote Christian Friedrich Daniel Schubart in 1784. The Mannheim orchestra was able to boast excellent players in both the string and wind sections.

Our series *Flute Music of the Mannheim School* is intended as an introduction to works by flautists (including J. Wendling and J. G. Mezger) and other Mannheim composers who wrote for the flute, with a selection of works still worthy of publication today.

Cover: Der pfälzische Kurfürst Karl Theodor (1743-1799), Mannheim, beim Flötenspiel, Gemälde von Johann Georg Ziesenis (1716-1777) (Bayerisches Nationalmuseum, München)

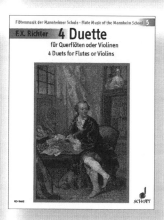

Heft 1/Volume 1
Johann Stamitz
Sonate G-Dur/G major
ED 8661

Heft 2/Volume 2
Johann Baptist Wendling
Sonate D-Dur/D major
ED 8662

Heft 3/Volume 3
Martin Friedrich Cannabich
Sonate D-Dur/D major
ED 8663

Heft 4/Volume 4
Johann Georg Mezger
Sonate G-Dur/G major
ED 8664

Heft 5/Volume 5
Franz Xaver Richter
4 Duette
ED 8665

Heft 6/Volume 6
Johann Wenzel Stamitz
6 Duette
ED 8666